Contents

Words outside Stage 2 are in a list on p. 59

The Magic Slippers

The king and queen in this story lived a long time ago. They loved each other very much and were very happy. They were still happier when a little son was born.

They thought that they would like a daughter next; but the second child was also a boy.

The queen said: 'Now there are two brothers waiting for our daughter.'

But the third child was also a boy, and this time they were a little sad. But they were sure that the fourth child would be a girl.

But no, another son was born.

And another.

And another.

And five more.

When their twelfth son was born, the king and queen were really very sad. Their sons were big and strong and good, and they loved them all. But they did want a little daughter so much.

At last, when their thirteenth child was born, it was a girl.

Words cannot tell how happy they were.

The queen called her twelve sons and showed them their beautiful little sister.

The king gave a great feast for everyone, rich and poor. The palace cooks worked night and day to get the food ready.

During the feast, the little princess was carried in for all the people to see.

Then the great door of the palace opened, and three fairies came in. No one spoke. They all knew that the fairies had come to give presents to the king's little daughter.

The first fairy said:

'I give her health: in all her life she will never have any illness.'

The second fairy said:

'I give her beauty: in all her life she will be beautiful.'

The third fairy said:

'I give her goodness: in all her life she will do nothing bad.'

Then there was a great light and they were gone.

Everyone began to talk, but soon the door opened again, and a little old woman dressed in black came in.

She ran across the floor, crying: 'Wait! Wait! Wait! We haven't finished yet!'

So everyone was quiet again.

The little old woman took out of her pocket two very small silver slippers. She put them on the little girl's feet.

Then she said: 'These are magic slippers. With these she will walk into people's hearts. Ha! Ha! Ha! Ha!'

Then she was gone, but for quite a long time they could hear her laughing: 'Ha! Ha! Ha!'

The wise men

All the people said: 'Walk into people's hearts? What does that mean?'

The king asked one of his wise men: 'Can you walk into people's hearts?'

The wise man looked down at his big feet and said: 'No, I can't.'

So the king said: 'What does it mean, then?'

And the wise man answered: 'I don't know.'

Then he asked another wise man: 'What does it mean?'

And the other wise man answered: 'I don't know.'

And the second wise man asked a third wise man, but even he didn't know.

So the king told them to go away and think about it. 'Tell me the answer before night,' he said.

The wise old men were not very pleased when they had to leave the feast, because they hadn't finished eating. But they had to go.

They went into a room where there were a lot of books; they thought that perhaps they might find the answer in one of the books. But they soon began to quarrel about it, and their beards went up and down and left and right; and two of them came too close to each other and their beards got mixed up. It took the others quite a long time to get them free. They had just finished when they heard a voice laughing.

'Ha! Ha! Ha!'

And there was the little old woman.

The answer

So the wise men asked the old woman what 'walk into people's hearts' meant, and she said:

'Walk into people's hearts means that she will make everyone love her.'

'Everyone?'

'Everyone! Men, women, boys, girls, dogs, cats, and elephants!'

Then she went, but she did not stop laughing: 'Ha! Ha! Ha!'

After the last 'Ha!' they looked at each other. The oldest one spoke:

'Now we can go and tell the king,' he said.

Another wise old man said: 'Shall we say that the old woman told us?'

Then all of them said: 'Ahem!'

The oldest one spoke again.

'No,' he said, 'we mustn't say that a woman knows more than we do. If we say that, no one will believe we are wise.'

Everyone will love her

So they went to the king and said: 'O great king, we have looked in all the books, and we have thought about it very carefully; and the meaning is this: the princess will make everyone love her.'

The king said: 'Everyone?'

'Everyone! Men, women, boys, girls, dogs, cats, and elephants!'

The king was pleased and said the old men could go on eating. The food was cold, so the cook brought some more.

Then the little princess was taken away to her mother, and the feast went on.

The princess grows up

Many years passed.

The queen died.

The little princess grew up as the fairies said. She was healthy and beautiful and good. She always wore the little slippers, and because they were magic slippers, they grew with her. As she grew bigger, the slippers grew bigger too.

The little old woman's words came true.

She walked into people's hearts. Everyone loved her.

Everyone. Men, women, boys, girls, dogs, cats and elephants.

The prince

When the princess was nearly fifteen, a prince who lived far away heard about her. He heard how everyone loved her. 'I'd like to marry her,' he thought.

So he set out on his long journey. He travelled alone, riding a white horse. After many days, he came to the country where the princess lived.

It was late. He was riding through a forest. His horse was very tired. He did not know where to stay the night. Then he saw a light through the trees, and soon he came to a little house.

He called: 'Is anyone there?'

A voice said: 'Come in.'

The little old woman

So he went in. Inside the house there was a little old woman dressed in black. The prince said: 'Please let me stay here tonight.'

'Certainly!' said the old woman. 'Put your horse in the hut at the back of the house, then come in again. Be careful, and don't fall over the cat.'

So the prince put his horse in the hut and gave him food and water. Then he went into the little house again.

The old woman was cooking some food. It smelt very good. Soon she put the food on the table and they both ate it.

She won't love you

When they had finished, the old woman said: 'You want to marry the princess.'

The prince was surprised. 'How do you know?' he asked. 'Are you a fairy?'

'Yes, I am,' she answered. 'Tell me about it; perhaps I'll help you.'

So the prince told her. When he had finished, she said: 'Young man, it will be very hard for you to win the princess.'

'But I'll do it,' he said.

'Don't be too sure,' said the old woman. 'Do you know why it will be hard?'

'No,' said the prince, 'but I hope you'll tell me.'

'Yes, I'll tell you,' she said, 'and I'll begin at the beginning. When she was born, I gave her some magic slippers. With them she has walked into people's hearts.'

The prince laughed; he knew what this meant.

'So,' went on the old woman, 'everyone loves her.'

'Everyone?'

'Everyone. Men, women, boys, girls, dogs, cats and elephants.'

'I see,' said the prince.

'Do you?' asked the old woman. 'I don't think you do. Everyone loves her, but she doesn't love anyone. You love her although you have never seen her, but she won't love you. That is part of the magic.'

The magic flower

'Then what can I do?' he asked.

'First,' said the old woman, 'you must bring me the magic slippers. Then I'll tell you what to do next.'

'How can I get them?' asked the prince.

'In the morning,' she answered, 'I'll give you a little blue flower. It's a magic flower, and with it you can put anyone to sleep. You must go to the king's palace, and when the soldier tries to stop you, touch him with the blue flower. Then he will fall asleep. After that you must find the princess, put her to sleep with the magic flower too, and take the slippers.'

So the next morning the old woman went out of the house. She found a little blue flower which grew in the forest. The prince took it, thanked her very much, and rode off to the palace.

The soldier at the gate cried out:

'Who's there?'

The prince touched him with the flower, and he fell asleep. Then the prince rode into the palace garden. He hid his horse among some trees, and walked on.

The prince takes the slippers

He heard laughing and talking, so he quickly climbed a tree and hid himself. Then he saw the princess with her ladies. She was very beautiful, and he loved her very much.

The princess and her ladies were playing a game called 'Hide-and-Seek'. In this game, one of the players hides, and the others try to find her. Soon the princess went to hide among some young trees.

The prince came down from his tree, and went to the place where the princess was hiding. He came up behind her, and so she did not hear him. He threw the magic blue flower at her, and she fell asleep at once. Then he took her slippers and put them in his pocket.

He got on his horse again, and rode back to the old woman's house.

The old woman said:

'You mustn't wear the slippers yourself. If you do, all the ladies will fall in love with you.'

'No, no!' said the prince, shutting his eyes.

'You must keep one slipper in your pocket, then the magic will work on one person only. I will keep the other slipper.'

The lost slippers

In the palace garden, the princess's ladies looked for a long time, but they couldn't find her. At last they did find her, asleep among the young trees.

They woke her very gently.

When she sat up, she said: 'Where are my slippers?'

No one knew.

They all went back to the palace and told the king. 'Someone has taken my silver slippers,' the princess said. He was very angry. He sent his twelve sons, each with a company of soldiers, to travel all over the land to look for the person who had taken their sister's silver slippers. But they found nothing.

The princess was very unhappy. Every day she wept for her lost slippers. At last the king said: 'Any prince who finds the lost slippers may marry the princess.'

He didn't feel very sure about this, because the princess liked to do what she wished. 'Perhaps she won't want to marry the prince who finds the slippers,' he thought. But he didn't say it.

The singer

One day, servants came to the king and said: 'There's a singer at the gate.'

The king said: 'Let him come in. Perhaps he'll make the princess happy again.'

So the singer was brought in. It was the prince, really, and he had one of the silver slippers with him; it was in his pocket, but no one knew that.

The prince began to play, and he sang songs of war, and songs to make you laugh, and songs of love.

Soon the princess began to laugh. When he stopped, she said:

'Sing again! Sing again.!

When the king saw her laughing, he was very pleased. The twelve brothers were also very pleased. The king said:

'Give this man a hundred pieces of gold.'

But the prince said:

'O King, I don't want gold.'

'You don't want gold?' said the king. 'Everyone wants gold.'

'You don't want gold?' said the twelve brothers.

'No,' said the prince.

'Then what do you want?' the king asked.

The prince looked at the princess; and she looked at him; and he knew that the magic slipper had done its work. So he said: 'There is only one thing in the world that I want.'

'And what is that?' the king asked.'

'To marry the princess.'

'May I speak?'

'WHAT?' cried the king.

'WHAT?' cried the twelve brothers.

'You, a singer who goes from house to house, you want to marry the princess?'

'Let's throw him out!' said the twelve brothers.

'Take him away,' the king ordered, 'and cut off his head.'

But the princess began to weep again.

'Oh, all right, all right!' the king said. 'Let him keep his head.'

So the princess stopped weeping.

The king didn't know what to do. He asked the princess: 'What shall I do with this man?'

And she answered: 'Let him marry me.'

'WHAT?' cried the king.

'WHAT?' cried the twelve brothers.

'Bah!' the king said angrily, 'you must marry the prince who finds your slippers. A lot of princes are on their way to try.'

The princess said: 'I don't want the old slippers any more, I only want to marry the singer.'

The prince said: 'May I speak?'

'No!' cried the king.

'No!' cried the twelve brothers.

'Yes!' said the princess.

Tomorrow—or...

Then the prince said quietly: 'I'll bring back the slippers.'

'But you aren't a prince,' said the king.

'The princess doesn't want a prince.'

The king said:

'Hmmmmmmmm!'

The king thought that the singer couldn't find the slippers. He still didn't know that the singer was really a prince.

'All right,' said the king, 'go and find the slippers, and when you have found them we'll see what can be done.'

'No. I'll marry the princess first, and then I'll give her the slippers.'

'WHAT?' cried the king.

'WHAT?' cried the twelve brothers.

Then they all began to talk at once. There was a great noise. Every time the king said the words 'Cut off his head' the princess began to cry, so he had to stop saying it. At last he said:

'HO!'

And everyone was quiet.

'The marriage will be tomorrow. After that there will be a feast. You, singer, will give the princess her silver slippers before the feast begins. If you don't, your head will be cut off.'

This time the princess did not weep. She laughed. Then she looked at the prince, and the prince looked into her eyes, and laughed too.

'Do you hear?' said the king. 'If you haven't got the slippers tomorrow, you'll lose your head.'

Then he marched out of the hall, and the twelve brothers marched after him.

Married

The next day there were fifty cooks cooking in the king's kitchen. There were fifty gardeners bringing in flowers. There were fifty servants helping the princess and her ladies to dress.

All the people put on their best clothes. The twelve brothers put on their best clothes. The king put on his best crown, but he looked very angry. The twelve brothers looked very angry.

So the prince and the princess were married.

After the marriage, everyone went to the great hall. First came the ladies and gentlemen; then the twelve brothers; then a man carrying an axe; then the king; and lastly the prince and princess.

When they were all there, the king said: 'Now, cut off his head. Then take away the body and we can get on with the feast.'

He said this because he was sure that the singer had not found the slippers. The man raised his axe and walked slowly across the hall to the prince; but just as he was going to cut off his head, the prince laughed and took the silver slipper out of his pocket.

'Here it is!'

The man with the axe was so surprised that his face went black and he couldn't speak, and they had to take him outside and give him a drink of water.

'Bah!' said the king, 'that's only one slipper. Where's the other?'

'Here it is!' said a voice, and there was the little old woman with the other slipper. 'Open the door,' she said, 'and see what you will see. Ha! Ha! Ha!'

So they opened the door, and there they saw a golden coach with six horses to pull it. The prince's father and mother were in it.

The king asked them to the feast. He was very glad that the singer who had married his daughter was really a prince.

Then the prince took the princess back to his own country, and his father and mother went too. And they all lived very happily.

The Beautiful Horse

Once upon a time there was a wise old merchant. His name was Abdul Hamid. He had a very beautiful Arab horse, and he wanted to sell it.

This horse could run faster than any other horse in the country. But the merchant wanted to sell it for three hundred pieces of gold. No one could pay so much.

One day a young man came to the merchant. His name was Aziz. He said:

'I am of good family, but I am very poor and I cannot buy the horse. Still, if you give me the horse, you won't lose anything. I am going to a far country, and everything that I get there I will give you.'

Abdul Hamid thought for a long time and pulled his beard. Then he said:

'All right. You can take the horse.'

So Aziz got on the horse and rode away to a far country. After a time he came to a great city. As he rode past the palace, the king was standing at the window. The king saw the beautiful horse. At once he wanted to have it.

So he sent servants to bring Aziz to the palace.

The king said: 'How much is that horse? I want to buy it.'

Aziz answered: 'It is nine hundred pieces of gold.'

'That's too much. But go away now, and come again tomorrow. Then we can talk about this again.'

The king's daughter

When Aziz had gone, the king called his wise men together. He said: 'The horse is the finest I have ever seen, but the price is too high.'

'Yes, the price is too high,' they all said.

But there was one man who wanted to please the king. He said: 'When the king speaks to the young man tomorrow, let all the young ladies in the palace be there. Surely he will fall in love with one of them, and then he will not care about the horse. So the king can buy it for much less.'

Next day when Aziz rode into the palace garden there were many ladies there. They were all very beautiful. Aziz did not look at them. But some of the ladies fell in love with him. Aziz still asked for nine hundred pieces of gold for his horse.

Then the king called his wise men again, and the man who wanted to please the king thought of another plan.

'My plan,' he said, 'was good, but it was not good enough. If he sees the king's daughter, he will remember nothing. Then the king can buy the horse.'

So the next day the king sat at the gate of the palace with his daughter. At noon Aziz came again to show the beauty of the horse. As he rode past the king, he saw the king's daughter. She looked at him. They fell in love with each other. She came nearer to look at the horse. Aziz told her quickly that if he sold the horse he must give the money to Abdul Hamid.

Out of the city

The princess looked up at him and said: 'O, my love! In my father's palace I have a coat. It is covered with gold and jewels. It has nine pockets, and in each pocket there are nine hundred pieces of gold. It's very hot now. Say "It's very hot. I feel ill." Then I'll go to get some water.'

So Aziz said, 'I feel ill,' and asked for water. The wise men heard him. The king's daughter went into the palace. She came out again wearing her gold coat and carrying a golden cup of water.

Aziz quickly raised her on to the horse in front of him. Then he rode out of the city.

All the king's men called for their horses and rode after Aziz. They tried to catch him, but they couldn't: no horse could run as fast as his. So they came back to the palace. The king was very angry.

Aziz and the princess rode on. The country was very beautiful, and they were very happy.

One day Aziz remembered Abdul Hamid and cried: 'Oh! I am an unhappy man!'

'What is the matter?'

Aziz keeps his word

He told her about Abdul Hamid.

Then he said: 'I said I would give him everything that I won with the horse. So the pieces of gold belong to him and the coat and the golden cup and even you, my love.'

'Why? You didn't win me, but I, a king's daughter, gave myself to you. So, we won't go to Abdul Hamid, but we'll stay here in the mountains, and be happy.'

But Aziz said:

'No. I gave my word, and I must keep it.'

They rode along quietly, and at the end of the journey they found Abdul Hamid.

Aziz said to him: 'Good day, Abdul Hamid. I have come back from a far country. I gave you my word: "I will give you everything that I get there." Here is a golden cup, and a golden coat with many pieces of gold in it. I bring you this lady too. She is the king's daughter, whom I love.'

Abdul Hamid was a wise old man; he thought for a long time and pulled his beard. Then he said: 'Truly, you have done well. The coat shall be mine and the cup shall be mine, and half the gold too. But you take half the gold and the horse and the lady.'

So Aziz and the princess were married and lived happily ever after.

The Gatekeeper's Daughter

Once upon a time there was a king who had three sons. They were all very strong, good-looking and clever. The king hoped that they would marry good, wise and beautiful princesses.

The king's palace was in a big garden. Around the garden was a high wall with one gate in it. The man who opened and shut this gate lived in a little house beside the gate.

The gatekeeper was not a rich man. The king didn't pay him very much money. The ladies and gentlemen who went to the palace never even spoke to him.

The gatekeeper had a daughter. Her name was Ann.

Ann was very kind to people, animals and birds. She was very kind to poor and sick people. If a poor man came to the house, she gave him some of her food, although she never had very much food herself. Everyone loved her because she was so very good and kind.

The youngest prince

One day the youngest prince went out riding. The

gatekeeper opened the gate, and the prince rode quickly out. He didn't look at the gatekeeper or at the gatekeeper's daughter. He couldn't look at anyone because he had to watch his horse: if people came too near, the horse kicked them. After some time, he thought he would go home. But on the way back the horse hurt his foot. So the prince had to get off the horse and walk. He saw some people standing outside the gatekeeper's house. There was a poor man and woman and their child.

'Who are these people?' asked the prince.

'They are my friends,' answered the gatekeeper's daughter.

Then the prince saw that the poor woman was weeping.

'Why are you weeping, my good woman?' he asked.

At first the poor woman was afraid to speak. But the gatekeeper's daughter took her by the hand and told her to answer the prince.

So she said: 'O Prince, my tears are tears of happiness. My child was ill and nearly died, but Ann was made him well. She is very wise.'

'I am very glad to hear that,' said the prince. 'Now, take your son home, and take care of him.'

The gatekeeper's daughter

So the poor people went home quite happy, and the prince said to Ann:

'Can you make my horse well again? He has hurt his foot.'

'I'll try,' she answered.

'Be careful,' he said, 'my horse may kick you. Sometimes he bites people when he doesn't know them.'

'I don't think he'll bite me,' said Ann.

She went up to the horse and spoke to him, and he followed her quite gently. She washed the horse's foot and put some oil on it. Then she said: 'Your horse will be well in two days.'

The prince went home, thinking about the gatekeeper's daughter.

After that he saw the gatekeeper's daughter often. Each time he learnt more about her. He learnt how kind and good she was, and how wise, and he saw that she was also beautiful.

After a long time he went to the king and said: 'Father, I want to get married.'

At first the king was very pleased to hear it, because he thought the prince wanted to marry a princess. So he said: 'Tell me which princess you wish to marry, and I'll send a letter to her father.'

But the prince said: 'I don't want to marry a princess, I want to marry the gatekeeper's daughter.'

When the king heard that, he was very angry.

'No! No!' he said. 'My sons must all marry princesses! What? Marry the gatekeeper's daughter? Never! I'll find a wife for you.'

'But I want to marry the gatekeeper's daughter and no one else.'

The king was very angry, and shut the prince up in the palace.

The eldest son

The king then called his eldest son to him and said: 'My son, you must go and find a wife. I will give you horses and money and servants. Travel, and find the wisest and most beautiful princess in the world and marry her. Then you shall be king after my death.'

So the prince set out and travelled for a very long time. In those days travelling was very hard, and the eldest prince took two years on his journey. He heard that there was a beautiful princess in India. People said that she was the most beautiful princess in the world. She was also good and wise. She was the daughter of a maharajah. After two years he reached India, and he came to the palace of the maharajah.

The maharajah was glad to see him and gave a great feast.

After three days the prince asked the maharajah for his daughter in marriage.

The maharajah said: 'If I give you my daughter in marriage, what will you do?'

'I will take her back to my father's country.

When I become king, she will be queen.'

'No,' said the maharajah. 'I love my daughter very dearly. I won't let her go away. If you marry her, you must stay in this country.'

This made the prince very sad; so the maharajah told him to go into the garden and think carefully about it.

The Maharajah's daughter

Now the prince had not seen the maharajah's daughter because she lived in the women's part of the palace. But her women told her about the prince. They said he was very good-looking. This made her want to see him. They told her that he was walking in the garden; so she looked out of her window.

Just then the prince looked up. They saw each other and fell in love. The prince knew that he must stay in India.

So he went to the maharajah. He couldn't say that he had seen the princess, because the maharajah would be angry. He said that he would stay in India because he wanted to marry the maharajah's daughter so much.

The maharajah was very glad. He gave a great feast for seven days and seven nights, and the prince and his daughter were married. Everyone was very happy.

After the marriage the prince sent a servant home to tell the king. The king was very sad. He knew that he would never see his son again.

So he sent for the second prince and said:

'My son, I will give you money and horses and servants. Travel, and find the wisest and most beautiful princess in the world, and marry her. Then you shall be king after my death.'

The second son

So the second prince set out on his travels. After two years he came to India and visited his brother at the palace of the maharajah. He stayed there for some time; then he went on his journey again.

On the way people told him about a most wise and beautiful princess who lived a long way to the East. They said that she was the daughter of the emperor of China.

So after another year he came to China and went to the emperor's palace.

The emperor was glad to see him and gave a great feast.

After three days the prince asked the emperor for his daughter in marriage.

The emperor said: 'If I give you my daughter in marriage, what will you do?'

'I will take her back to my father's country. When I become king she will be queen.'

'No,' said the emperor. 'I love my daughter very dearly. I won't let her go away. If you marry her you must stay in this country.'

This made the prince very sad. So the emperor told him to go for a walk and think carefully about it.

The emperor's daughter

Now the prince had not seen the emperor's daughter. He walked in the city and thought about her. He walked in the beautiful streets and heard people talking about the emperor's daughter.

'She can read all the books in the world.'

'She's so wise that the emperor himself sometimes asks her to help him.'

'She's so beautiful that the moon and the sun are her servants.'

Just at this time the emperor's daughter was carried past. She had heard about this prince from the West who wanted to marry her. So she looked out.

Just then the prince looked up. They saw each other and fell in love. Then the prince said:

'I must marry the princess and stay in China.

The emperor was very glad. He gave a great feast for twenty-one days, and the prince and his daughter were married. Everyone was very happy.

After the marriage the prince sent his servant home to tell the king. The king was very sad.

'What shall I do?' he wondered.

At last he went to the room where the youngest prince was shut up because he wanted to marry the gatekeeper's daughter.

'My son,' he said, 'both your brothers have gone to live in other countries. So you must forget about the gatekeeper's daughter and marry a princess.'

But the youngest prince said: 'I don't want to

marry a princess. I want to marry the gatekeeper's daughter.'

The wise men think

Then the king was very angry. He went back to the palace and called together all his wise men.

He said to them: 'What shall I do? My two eldest sons have left me, and my youngest son still wants to marry the gatekeeper's daughter. Shall I put her to death?'

The wise men thought about this. Then they said: 'No, O king, you must not put her to death, because she has done nothing bad.'

'What shall I do then?'

The wise men thought for a long time. Then they all went to see the gatekeeper's daughter. After that the oldest and wisest man of them all (he was nearly a hundred years old) said:

'If I may go and think about it, in three days I will find an answer to this question.'

The king agreed, and the old man went home. He read some very old books; and he thought and thought and thought. For three days he did not eat or drink. At the end of that time he went to see the king.

'I have found the answer,' he said.

The answer

Then the king sent for all the other wise men. He

also sent for his youngest son. They all waited to hear the old man speak.

He began: 'O king, I have read many old books. I learnt that the greatest things in the world are truth and kindness. The gatekeeper's daughter has these things more than any other person in the country. In this way she is greater than any princess. Only one thing is needed. She must be made a princess. Then the prince can marry her.'

All the old men said that it was a very wise answer. The prince was very pleased. The king was not very pleased, but he wasn't angry.

So the king made a law. This law said that everyone must call the gatekeeper's daughter Princess Ann. Then the king gave a great feast which lasted a whole month, and the youngest prince married the gatekeeper's daughter. They lived happily ever after.

Florio and Floria

Once upon a time there was a king who had a son and a daughter. Their names were Florio and Floria. Their mother died, and the king married another wife. The new queen was not unkind to Florio and Floria, because she knew that the king would be angry; but she certainly didn't love them.

There was an old servant who loved them very much. She had been their nurse since they were babies.

Then the king died. Florio should have been the next king; but the queen wanted to rule the country. The first thing she did was to send away the old nurse, leaving Florio and Floria with no one to love them.

The queen wanted to kill Florio, but one of the servants told him; so one night he ran away. He found the old nurse's house. She hid him there, and the queen could not find him.

The queen was very angry and shut Floria up in a room at the top of a high tower.

One day a prince of another country was travelling through the city. His name was Prince

Roland. He came riding past the tower, and he saw Floria at her window. She looked very sad and very beautiful, and he thought: 'I must find out why she is so sad and try to help her.'

So he climbed up to the window. Floria told him about the queen, and how her brother had run away.

Prince Roland said: 'I'll come back after dark with horses and servants, and take you to my father and mother.'

'Kill Floria'

That day, the queen was driving round the city; and she saw Prince Roland climb down from the tower and ride away. She could not see who he was; he was too far away.

She went straight to the tower. She was very angry.

'Who has been here?' she asked.

Floria did not answer. She knew the queen would kill Roland if she could, so she said nothing.

'Answer me at once! I saw a man riding away. Who is he?'

Still Floria did not speak.

Then the queen said: 'Bad girl! Tell me at once, or you shall die!'

Floria said nothing. So the queen sent for two soldiers and told them to kill Floria.

They held cloths over her face until she lay still.

Then the queen was afraid. The people loved Floria, and if they knew how she died they would be very angry. Perhaps they would kill the queen.

So she sent for the Prime Minister. When he came, he found her weeping. Of course she was not really weeping; but she *seemed* to be weeping.

'Oh, Prime Minister!' she said, 'poor dear little Princess Floria is dead! She was ill for several days, and I took care of her myself.'

The Prime Minister was very sad, and (unlike the queen) he was truly sad.

'Tonight,' said the queen, 'her body will lie in the church, and four soldiers will keep watch.'

The Prime Minister went away.

Too dangerous

When the people heard that Princess Floria was dead, they were very sad, and there was weeping all over the land.

When Prince Roland heard, he fell to the ground like a dead man, and his servants quickly carried him away to his own country.

When the old nurse heard, she wept, and she told Florio. Now Florio, too, was very sad to hear of his sister's death.

'I must see her dear face for the last time,' he said.

'You can't do that,' said the nurse.

'Yes, I can,' said Florio. 'Tonight four soldiers

will keep watch. They'll know me. I'll tell them to open the coffin and let me see my sister's face again.'

'It's too dangerous,' said the nurse. 'They may take you to the queen.'

'I must go.'

The nurse was afraid. She knew the queen would kill him if she could. So she said: 'I'll let you see your sister. But you must do what I tell you; and you must not go out of the house.'

Florio asked the nurse what she was going to do, but she wouldn't tell him.

In the church

Floria's body was put into a beautiful silver coffin. It was carried to the church. All the great ladies and gentlemen followed, and the bad queen was also there, weeping (or seeming to weep).

The coffin was put in the church and covered with flowers. The four soldiers took their places. Then all the other people went home until next day.

In the night the four soldiers heard a fearful sound. A voice seemed to say:

'Woohoooooooo!... Woohoooooooo!...'

They were very much afraid. Their faces were white with fear. Then they saw a green light coming along the floor. Then they heard the fearful voice again:

'Weeheeeeeee!... Weeheeeeeee!...'

It was too much. The soldiers ran away.

The nurse was sitting on the floor with a green light. It was the green light which made the soldiers afraid. She had made the noises too. As soon as they were gone, she stood up.

She opened the coffin, took out Floria's body, and filled up the coffin with stones and cloth. She put the stones in cloth so that they would not make a noise when the coffin was carried. Then she carried Floria's body to her house, and called Florio to come and look at his dead sister.

She's alive!

The nurse went away and left Florio alone with Floria's body. While he was looking sadly at her, he thought he saw her move. He looked more closely, and she *was* moving.

He called out: 'Nurse! Nurse! Come quickly!' The nurse came. He said: 'Look nurse, look! She's alive!'

The nurse looked. Florio was right.

Floria opened her eyes.

How happy they were! They quickly brought hot water and food and warm clothes. They rubbed her feet and hands. They put her to bed.

Soon she could talk. She was so glad to see her brother again. She told them how the queen had ordered the soldiers to kill her. She asked them about Prince Roland, but the nurse did not know anything about him.

Next day all the people went to the church. They took away only a coffin full of stones, but they didn't know that. Of course the soldiers never told anyone what happened in the night.

So for a time the brother and sister lived with the nurse. They never went out in the city, because the nurse was afraid that the queen would find out.

Prince Roland

One day, when the nurse went to buy some food, she met a traveller and his wife. The traveller belonged to Prince Roland's country, but the wife belonged to the city. The wife had come back to visit her family. She and the nurse were old friends. They were very pleased to see each other.

The nurse asked about Prince Roland.

'Oh,' said the traveller's wife, 'it's very sad! He came here and fell in love with the Princess Floria; and when she died, he fell ill. We know he's going to die, and we are very unhappy. We're very sorry for our king and queen, because he's their only son.'

The nurse went home and told Floria. Floria wanted to go at once to Prince Roland, but her brother asked her not to go. He was afraid that the queen would find out.

At last the nurse said: 'I've got a plan.'

They asked her what it was, but she would not tell them.

The two women

Now we must see what was happening to Prince Roland.

He was very ill. His mother and father and all his friends were very sad. All the wise men in the country tried to help him, but they couldn't do anything.

'Nothing can be done,' they said, 'he's going to die.'

One day two women came to the palace gate. Nobody could see what they were like because their faces were covered. One was big, and one was small.

A soldier stopped them. 'You can't come in,' he said.

The big woman answered: 'We are wise women, and we have come to make the prince well again.'

The soldier laughed. 'Bah!' he said, 'the wisest men in the country can't do that, so what can you do?'

One of the king's servants was passing and heard all this. He said: 'Let them come in. Perhaps they can use magic. Who knows?'

'Leave me alone'

So the soldier let them in, and the servant took them to the king.

The king asked: 'Who are you?'

Again the big woman answered:

'We are wise women and we have come to make the prince well again.'

'No one can do that. But you may try. Perhaps you can use magic.'

So he opened the door of the prince's room, and they went in.

The big woman said: 'Everyone must go, and leave us with the sick man.'

The wise men didn't want to go, but the king made them do so.

When they were all gone, the big woman shut the door. Now this woman was really the old nurse. She spoke to the prince.

'We have come to make you well again,' she said.

'Leave me alone,' said the prince, 'and let me die. Floria is dead, and I don't want to live. I think I'm dead already.'

A happy ending

The nurse told the small woman to uncover her face, then she took her by the hand, and showed her to the prince.

'Now I know that I am dead,' he said, 'because I see Floria.'

'I *am* Floria,' she said. 'I am alive and well. Now you must get well too.'

Then the prince became quite well and strong again. He stood up and took Floria in his arms. The nurse opened the door, and in came the king and queen.

How surprised they were, and how glad!

A lot of people were standing round the door, and they told the servants. The servants told the soldiers. The soldiers told the people outside the palace. Soon all the people in the country knew.

All the bells rang. There were great feasts. People danced and sang for happiness.

Roland and Floria were married.

When the bad queen heard that Floria was still alive, she was so afraid that she fell down dead.

Then Florio went to the palace and was made king at once.

Roland and Floria came to see him. They brought the nurse with them. She came to live in the king's palace. Sometimes she went to stay with Roland and Floria.

They all lived happily ever after.

The Flying Mare

There was once an Arab named Mustafa. He was a merchant. Mustafa was very rich. He had a great many horses and camels; he had a great many servants and a large family, and beautiful tents to live in and rich food to eat.

There was also a poor man named Husain. He was very very poor, but he had one thing, and that was a mare. Arab horses are very beautiful, and they can run very fast. This mare was nearly the same colour as the sand of the desert. So when Husain rode across the desert, people who were far off couldn't see the mare, and when they saw Husain moving very quickly, they thought he was flying. So they called Husain's mare 'The Flying Mare'.

The Flying Mare

One evening Mustafa sat at the door of his tent, looking across the desert. Beside him was Mahmud, his head servant. Suddenly they saw Husain riding. They couldn't see the mare, because she was the same colour as the desert, and Mustafa thought Husain was flying. He was very surprised.

'What's this?' he said.

'It's Husain,' said Mahmud, 'and he's riding the Flying Mare.'

Then, as Husain came nearer, Mustafa could see the Flying Mare. He saw how beautiful she was, and how strong, and how fast she ran; she seemed truly to fly over the desert.

'I must have that mare,' said Mustafa. 'Go and buy her for me.'

I am a poor man

So Mahmud went to meet Husain, and spoke to him; and after their evening prayer he asked Husain to eat with Mustafa and all his followers.

When they had finished their food, they sat round the fire, and told stories. It is often very cold in the desert at night, and people need a fire to keep them warm. No one spoke about the mare that night.

Next morning, Mahmud began to talk to Husain about the mare.

'What will you do,' he asked, 'if your beautiful mare is ill?—if she dies?'

'God is good,' said Husain. 'I am a poor man.'

'How much better,' went on Mahmud, 'to have money. My master is very rich. He will pay you a lot of money for your mare.'

'I don't want to sell her,' answered Husain.

Mahmud told Mustafa what Husain had said.

'Speak to him again,' said Mustafa, 'and say I will give him a horse as well as the price of his mare. I must have the mare. If I don't have her I won't sleep.'

'I won't sell her'

So Mahmud went back to Husain.

'My master will give you a horse,' he said, 'as well as the money for your mare.'

'Tell your master,' said Husain, 'that I won't sell her.'

Mahmud went to Mustafa and said: 'He won't sell the mare.'

'Say I'll give him a great deal of gold,' said Mustafa, 'a thousand gold pieces.'

Mahmud went back and offered Husain a thousand pieces of gold for his mare.

Husain answered: 'I've had my mare since she was born. She knows my voice, and she knows my step, and she is to me like a daughter. I won't sell her for ten times ten thousand gold pieces.'

When Mustafa heard this, he was angry; he still tried to make Husain sell the mare. But Husain wouldn't sell.

'I must help him'

At last Mustafa thought: 'I must get the mare, even if I have to do something very bad.'

He waited until Husain was getting ready to go away. Then he cut off his own beard and put on old clothes, and rode into the desert, to a place that Husain must pass. Here he let his horse go, and the horse went back to his friends. Then Mustafa lay down as if he were very ill.

Soon Husain came riding along on his Flying Mare. He saw Mustafa, but he didn't know him, and he thought:

'Here is a poor traveller, lost in the desert. He's very ill. I must stop and help him, or he'll die.'

So he stopped. He gave Mustafa a drink of water. Then he raised him, and put him on the mare's back. Mustafa didn't speak.

Husain walked beside the mare. He led her with one hand, and held Mustafa with the other.

After about two miles, Mustafa said: 'Thank you for your help. Now I'm better, don't tire yourself. Take away your hand.'

'Don't tell them'

So Husain took his hand away from Mustafa's back. Then Mustafa hit him on the face, and hit him again and again until he fell down.

Mustafa rode away.

Husain called his mare. She knew his voice and came back. Mustafa tried to make her go on, but she wouldn't. Then Husain saw that it was Mustafa and he said:

'Mustafa! Truly this is a bad thing that you have done. But you are rich and powerful, and I can do nothing. If I call my mare back now, you will find another way to take her. But one thing you must not do. When you show this beautiful mare to your friends, you must never tell them how you got her.'

'Why mustn't I tell them that?'

'Don't tell them,' said Husain, 'that I found you

on the ground like a dying man, and that you took my mare when I tried to help you. If people know that, they will never again help sick or lost travellers in the desert. They'll be afraid to. They'll think that all lost travellers are thieves like you. And so, many good people will be left to die.'

Other people

Mustafa did not answer. He was thinking:

'I have taken this poor man's mare. He has nothing left. But he doesn't think of himself; he thinks about other people and how to help them. He's a very good man, and I have been very bad.'

So Mustafa was sorry.

'Take back your mare. Truly I have done a bad thing.'

Husain answered: 'The bad thing was not finished. Let us forget that it was ever begun.'

'If you can forgive me,' said Mustafa, 'come back and eat with me.'

So Mustafa and Husain became friends.

The Story of Pulau Sireh

Not far from Malaysia there is an island called Pulau Sireh. Many years ago, this island was ruled by a sultan, Sultan Mahmud.

He had many sons and daughters, but all his sons were killed in war. Then a great sickness came to the island, and the daughters died. Only one daughter was left, and her name was Tengku Zainab.

The sultan was an old man, and he loved his daughter very much; and because he had no son, he dressed her as a boy and tried to think that she was a boy. He said that she was to rule the island after his death.

She liked dressing as a boy, because she could go where she liked and play, instead of having to live in the women's part of the palace. But all the ladies who lived in the palace said that it was a very bad thing.

Tengku Zainab

The son of the sultan's brother lived on Pulau Sireh, and his name was Tengku Awang. He wanted to be sultan; so he thought the best thing to do was to marry Tengku Zainab. All the ladies thought it would be a very good thing, and they told her that she ought to marry Tengku Awang. But Tengku Zainab did not want to marry him, and she told the sultan about it. So the sultan said that Awang couldn't marry her. Tengku Awang was very angry about this, and he tried to think of a plan to hurt the sultan and Tengku Zainab.

At that time there were a great many pirates in the seas around Malaysia. In their fast warships they caught merchant ships and took everything from them.

The visitor

One of the countries to which Sultan Mahmud sent merchant ships was called Perantak. The Sultan of Perantak thought it would be a good thing to meet Sultan Mahmud, and ask his help to fight against the pirates. So he sent his Laksamana, the man who led all his warships, to visit Sultan Mahmud.

Sultan Mahmud was very pleased to see the Laksamana, and treated him very well. He said he would help the Sultan of Perantak to fight against the pirates. The Laksamana stayed on Pulau Sireh for seven days.

All this time Tengku Awang was watching very carefully. He was trying to find a way to make himself sultan. So, on the seventh day, he went to the Laksamana and said:

'I am your friend, and I have come to tell you

that the sultan wants to kill you. You are going to say goodbye to him today. When he raises his hand, that is to tell his soldiers to kill you; so when he raises his hand you and your men must fight.'

The Laksamana thanked him. Then someone came to take him to the sultan to say goodbye.

A great fight

The sultan did not want to kill the Laksamana at all. He wanted to give him a present to take to the Sultan of Perantak. So, when the Laksamana stood before him, he raised his hand to call the servants who were carrying the present.

When the Laksamana saw him raise his hand, he thought that the sultan was telling the soldiers to kill him. He ran at the sultan with his *keris*.

Then there was a great fight. All the Laksamana's men stood round him and fought against the sultan's men. The Laksamana was killed. Nearly all his men were killed, and only a few reached the boats, and sailed back to Perantak to tell the story.

The sultan was dying.

He called together all the great men of the land. Tengku Awang came with the others. The sultan told them that Tengku Zainab must rule Pulau Sireh. They all said they would help her. Even Tengku Awang said it, though he meant to make himself sultan as soon as he could.

The stockade

Then the sultan died.

Everyone was very sad, because he had been a good man. Zainab was very sad. She stopped playing, and began to think what was the best thing to do. She called all the good and brave men, and asked them to help her.

She said: 'Very soon the people of Perantak will come and fight us. We must be ready for them.

What shall we do?'

The men said, 'We ought to cut down a lot of trees and build a stockade at the mouth of the river. Then we should put food and water for many days inside the stockade.'

So they did that.

Then one day they saw a great many boats sailing to the island. Zainab put on her fighting coat, and they all got ready to fight the men of Perantak. They didn't go out and fight them at sea, because the Perantak people had more warships than the people of Pulau Sireh.

The leader of the Perantak army was Raja Hassan. He and his men tried to get into the stockade; but Zainab and her men fought bravely and kept them off. At sunset, they stopped fighting and went back to their boats.

The fight went on for three days, then Tengku Awang turned against his own people.

This was how he did it.

Tengku Awang's plan

The stockade had four sides. On one side was the sea, and the river ran on two other sides, but on the fourth side there was forest. Now an army couldn't fight on this side, because there were too many trees; so the stockade was not so strong on this side.

One night Tengku Awang went out of the stockade, and down to the sea. Then he went out to

Raja Hassan's boat.

He said: 'I'm your friend. I tried to help the Laksamana. What will you give me if I let you into the stockade?'

Raja Hassan answered: 'What do you want?'

' I want you to give me the young sultan, alive or dead, and make me sultan in his place.'

He didn't tell Raja Hassan that Zainab was a girl although she was dressed as a sultan in fighting dress.

Raja Hassan talked to his friends. Then he said: 'I'll give you the young sultan, alive or dead, and I'll make you sultan in his place, but you must send gold every year to the Sultan of Perantak.'

Tengku Awang said that he would do this. Then he told them what to do.

'You must come on to the island,' he said, 'not here, but farther away; and you must come at night, when no one can see you. Then go into the forest and come round carefully to the forest side of the stockade. I will wait for you there, and I'll let you in.'

Raja Hassan said he would do that, and then Tengku Awang went back to the island.

A girl!

Next night Raja Hassan and some of his men came to the forest side of the stockade, and Tengku Awang let them in. In the morning, Raja Hassan opened the big gate and let the rest of his men in, and there was a great fight.

Tengku Awang was killed; so he did not become sultan after all.

The Perantak men won, and Zainab was taken to Raja Hassan.

When she saw Raja Hassan she didn't remember that she was dressed as a man, and she was afraid. So she covered her face with her hands like a girl. When he saw this, Raja Hassan thought: 'This is a girl!' He asked some of the Pulau Sireh men if it was true, and they said yes.

So Raja Hassan sent for the ladies of the palace. They came, weeping and very much afraid. He told them to take Zainab away and look after her and dress her as a girl ought to be dressed.

Then he told his men not to burn the houses or take things from the people, but to keep quiet until he told them what to do. They were surprised, because after winning a fight, they always did what they liked.

'Never!'

Now Raja Hassan thought he would like to marry Zainab and become the ruler of Pulau Sireh; and he knew that the people would be glad if he stopped his soldiers from burning houses and doing other bad things.

So he sent for an old lady who lived in the palace. When she came, he told her that he wanted to marry Zainab. She was surprised, but she went to Zainab and told her.

'Please get ready,' she said, 'because the marriage must be soon. Then we shall be quiet again.'

'No!' cried Zainab. 'He can kill me if he likes, but I'll never marry him!'

Zainab changes her mind

The old lady talked and talked, but it was no good. Zainab wouldn't change her mind. The old lady didn't know what to do. She was afraid to tell Raja Hassan that Zainah wouldn't marry him. At last he sent for her, and she had to go.

'Have you told the women to get ready for the marriage?' he asked.

At first the old lady didn't know what to say, but after a time she told him. He was not angry, but said:

'All right. I'll wait a few days.'

Zainab was surprised that he wasn't angry and didn't try to *make* her marry him. So she changed her mind and said she would marry him.

The old lady was very pleased. She was a wise old lady, and she knew that this marriage would stop all the fighting.

Then everyone began to get ready for the marriage. The women cooked food for a great feast. The men cleaned up after the fight.

They lived for many years on Pulau Sireh, and they were very happy.

Questions

The Magic Slippers

1 Why were the king and queen sad when the twelfth son was born?
2 What presents did the fairies give to the little princess?
3 What did the people say when the little old woman had gone?
4 What did the king tell the wise men to do?
5 What did the wise men ask the little old woman?
6 What did the wise men tell the king?
7 How did the little princess grow up?
8 What happened when the princess was nearly fifteen?
9 Who was inside the house?
10 Why was it hard for the prince to win the princess?
11 What did the little old woman tell the prince to bring her?
12 How did the prince get the magic slippers?
13 How did the ladies find the princess?
14 Who was the singer really?
15 What did the princess ask the king to do?
16 What did the king tell the prince?
17 What did the king say when all the people were in the hall?
18 When the door was opened, what did the people see?

The Beautiful Horse

1 What did Aziz tell the merchant?
2 What happened to Aziz when he saw the king's daughter?
3 What did the princess tell Aziz about the coat?
4 What did Abdul Hamid take from Aziz?

The Gatekeeper's Daughter

1 What kind of a man was the gatekeeper?
2 Why was it that the prince could not look at anyone when he was riding?
3 What did the prince ask Ann to do?
4 What did the prince do after three days in the Maharajah's palace?
5 Why had not the prince seen the Maharajah's daughter?
6 After three days in the emperor's palace what did the second prince ask the emperor?

7 What did people say about the emperor's daughter?
8 How did the wise men stop the king from putting the gate-keeper's daughter to death? What did they say?
9 What law did the king make?

Florio and Floria

1 What happened after the king died?
2 As the queen was driving round the city, what did she see?
3 What happened to Prince Roland when he heard about Floria's death?
4 Who was making the noises that frightened the soldiers?
5 What happened as Florio looked at his sister's body?
6 What did the traveller's wife tell the nurse about Prince Roland?
7 Who came to the palace gate?
8 Who was the big woman?
9 Who was the small woman?

The Flying Mare

1 What did people call Husain's mare?
2 Why did Mustafa think that Husain was flying?
3 What did Mustafa ask Mahmud to say to Husain?
4 Why didn't Husain want to sell the mare?
5 What did Husain think when he saw Mustafa?
6 What happened as Husain took away his hand from Mustafa's back?
7 How did they become friends?

The Story of Pulau Sireh

1 Why did Tengku Zainab like being dressed as a boy?
2 What are pirates?
3 What did Tengku Awang say to the Laksamana?
4 What happened when the Laksamana saw the sultan raise his hand?
5 What is a stockade?
6 What did Tengku Awang do?
7 What did Zainab do when she saw Raja Hassan?
8 What did Raja Hassan want to do?
9 What did Raja Hassan say when the old lady told him that Zainab would not marry him?

List of extra words

all right *good; without difficulty; not in danger*

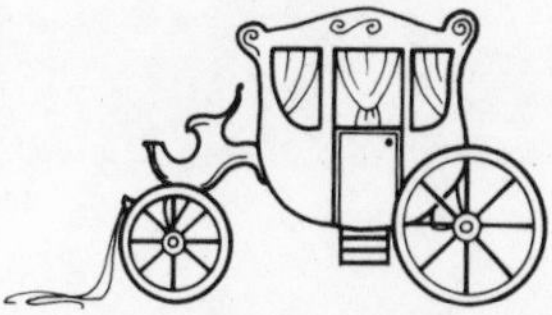

coach

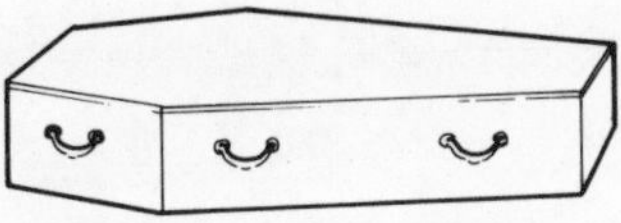

coffin

desert *land where no plant grows*

emperor *the ruler of a number of countries*

feast *a big meal with fine food*

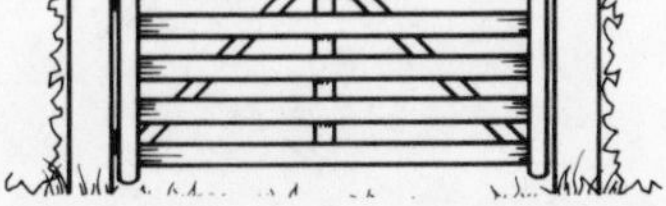

gate

keris/kri:s/ *a Malay sword*

maharajah *the ruler of a great country in India*

mare *a "she"-horse*

merchant *a man who buys and sells things in great numbers*

nurse *a woman who looks after a child for its mother*

pirate

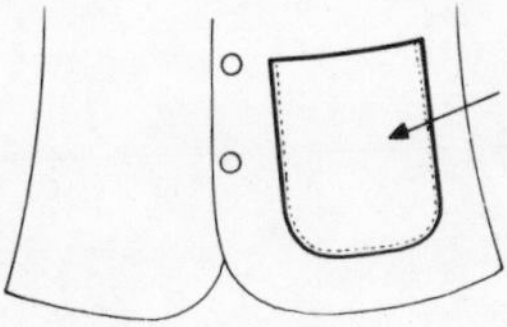

pocket

prime minister *the person who does the work of ruling a country for a king or queen*

stockade *a strong wall of wood* (see page 51)

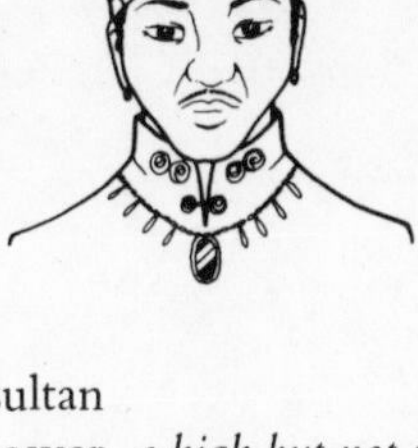

sultan

tower *a high but not very wide building* (see page 33)